Other Gift books in the series

To the most, most special Dad
To the most, most special Granddaughter
To the most, most special Grandma
Wishing you Happy Days
Thinking of You...

Published in 2014 by Helen Exley® in Great Britain.

The illustrations by Juliette Clarke and the design,
selection and arrangement © Helen Exley Creative Ltd 2014.
Words by Pam Brown © Helen Exley Creative Ltd 2014.
The moral right of the author has been asserted.

ISBN: 978-1-84634-709-2

12 11 10 9 8 7 6 5 4 3 2

Helen Exley®
16 Chalk Hill, Watford, Herts.
WD19 4BG, UK.
www.helenexley.com

You can follow us on and

To the Most, most special Sister

ILLUSTRATIONS BY JULIETTE CLARKE
WORDS BY PAM BROWN

HELEN EXLEY®

You...

Sometimes
you puzzle me.
Sometimes
you annoy me.
Sometimes
you unnerve me.
But always, always, always
you are my sister.
And I wouldn't swap you.

Patience

Love

Caring

Forgivenes

Sisters are the people we practice on,
the people who teach us about fairness
and kindness and caring.

Little sisters
are sent to keep us human
– and they do.

Anyone with a sister
is one up on everyone else
in social survival.

You and I...
We've learned over the years
patience and understanding,
love and forgiveness.

Top Supporter!

You graciously accept applause
and smile and smile
and look wonderful.
But your sister is standing by
with a bowl of hot water,
in which to soak your feet,
and a cup of tea.

Sisters cover for you.
And keep schtum.

Sisters can keep a secret
as long as is necessary
– which may be forever.

"**D**o you remember?"
brings back those summer skies,
the sweet, high song of larks,
the waist-high grasses.
The future charged with
goals and targets.

Sisters are bound together

There was something special
about walking up the road
with your sister's little hand
tucked into yours,
safe and secure and confident.

in a mesh of memories.

Chaos!

It is a proven fact that sisters need
the bathroom, the loo, the hairdryer,
the long mirror and the text book
at exactly the same time.

Nothing one has – dress, shoes,
tights, make-up – is safe from a
sister headed for a party.

A sister is naggings and needlings,
whispers and whisperings.
Bribery. Thumpings. Borrowings.
Breakings. Welcomings home.

"Help! Somebody!
She's got my vest!"

Surprise!

The gift bag
with the most outrageous surprise
is the one from your sister.

On special occasions sisters
give you the thing you saw and loved
six months ago and never guessed
she'd bought and smuggled out
behind your back.

When your sister is flat broke
she'll still come up with something
astonishing for your birthday.

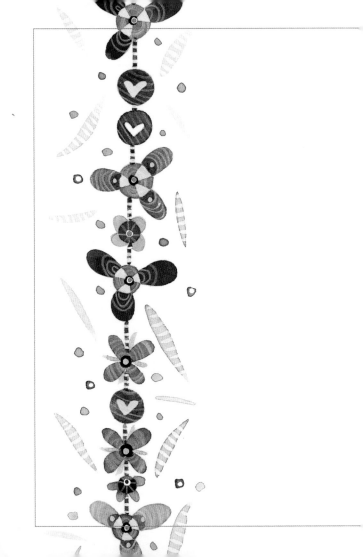

Friends get the slightly expurgated
version of your life.
Sisters know the actual truth.

Other people we know a little
or a lot about… as much as they reveal,
as much as we discover.
Only siblings know everything
about each other.

No matter how the world sees you –
your sister knows you as you really are.
And that is what keeps you human.

Unity

Despite the differences,
the rows, the jealousies,
we know a unity that
no one else can understand.
We know so much
about each other
– know the roots of every change.

You need not love each other –
or even like each other.
But you need each other.
Your roots are intertwined.

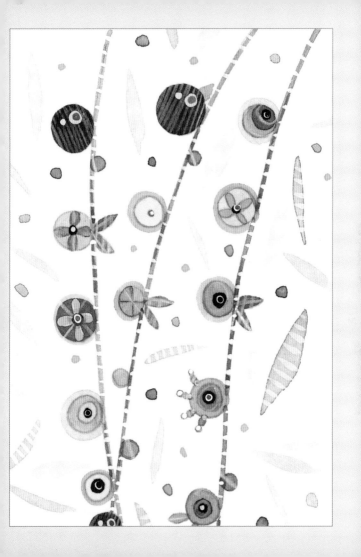

Sisters for all time

The sister crammed into
the doll's pram.
The sister on the swing.
The sister trailing behind
on the sponsored walk.
The sister flat in the mud.
The self same sister
who sits across the café table,
white-haired
and eating an éclair.
Smiling, kind,
unchanged.

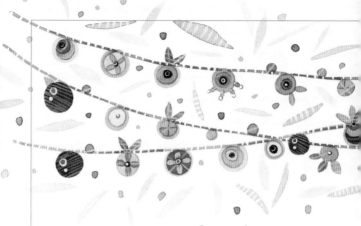

Without

What would I do without you
to weep on, to share secrets,
to unload anxieties,
to delight in something special
that's occurred?
What would success be
if you did not applaud?
And how could I bear disappointment

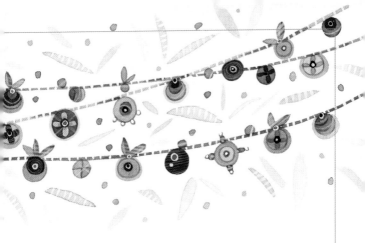

you

if you were not there to pick me up
and dust me down
and give me hope again?
I wish you happiness
and companionship – as much as all
you've given me.

Invariably – it's your sister
who first finds out what you've
been up to.

A sister is very rarely fooled.

Every sister has a fund of
embarrassing stories
she can bring out
at the most effective moment.

Knows it all

A sister knows all your best stories
better than you.
And is inclined to put you right!

Sisters know too much
about your past.
And they have memories
like elephants.

Who greets the news
of your most incredible achievement
with, "Good.
I told you that you could do it."?

What is the pleasure
in passing your finals if you have not got
a sister to hug?

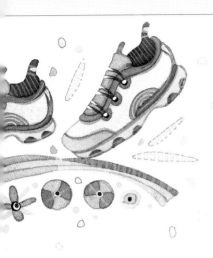

"If you fail,
I'll sigh for you.
If you succeed
I'll put out all the flags
and share
in your delight."

Understand...

Sisters disentangle problems
in arithmetic and knitting.
And when they're grown they listen
to your problems, your anxieties.

Sisters know
when to yell at you
– and when to
hug.

There's one person you can trust
to tell you the truth
about your looks,
your clothes, your new glasses.
Your sister.

We two have something special
that no one else has.
For we are sisters
and understand each other
just about completely.

The Awful Truth!

At the first sign of
incipient smugness or superiority sisters
douse you in cold water –
and shrink you back to your proper size.

A sister is usually
the only person who will tell you
the unvarnished truth.

Sisters remember things you
would rather forget.
In graphic detail… with proof.

One may be a star,
a Chief Executive
– successful and famous and rich.
But one's sister has
the family photo album.
And a long memory!

In times of trouble,
sisters scold
– but rescue you. And grin.
And make a cup of tea.

Sisterhood can lie dormant
for years – but suddenly
there is an emergency and hour-long
phone calls –
advice given and advice taken.

Rescues you!

For all the times you cleaned me up before Dad saw me. For helping me remember that awful nine times table.

For punching Herbert Johnson on the nose. For sewing up the hem of my best suit. Thank you!

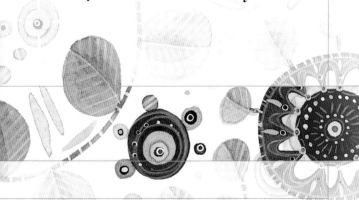

You borrowed my lipstick, my shoes, my tights…. Even my best party frock. You ate my chocolates. And I forgive you. *I have to.* *I borrowed yours.*

The worst nightmare for any sister
is to have borrowed, secretly,
your very best top – and spilled
blackcurrant juice down the front.

What would we do without
a sister to borrow from? Tights. Shoes.
Make-up. Parking fines.

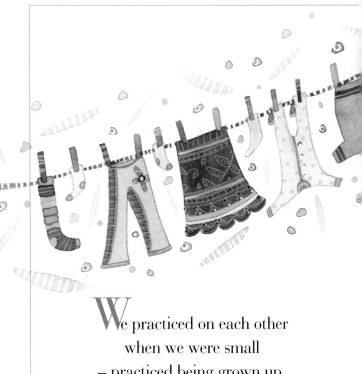

We practiced on each other
when we were small
– practiced being grown up.
Squabbled and made up.
Learned what it is to love
and how to help each other
through the bad times.

How small
we were

How small we were.
How vulnerable. And yet we had plans.
You and me together.

Once you get together
with your sister,
you're inclined to drift into
the kitchen, slip off your shoes –
and talk. And talk.

Talk! Talk

When you come through your
sister's door, you hang up all pretence
with your coat.

Sisters listen when no one else
has the time.

Talk!

Sisters don't need careful explanations.
They don't even need full sentences…

It's good to go out with friends
but, maybe best of all, it's good
to spend the day with a sister.
No need to impress
– she'd only laugh.

We bickered over little things.
We told tales, took ownership of each
other's things without permission.
And yet, sided with one another against
authority. Untangled homework.
Comforted each other.

A big sister blames you
for everything. Still, a dead beetle
in her bed evens things up!

CIVIL WAR!

We disagree all the time.
Remember things quite differently.
Disapprove of one another's choices.
Are maddened by each other's habits.
But we are vital
to each other's existence.

A shared past

You can rewrite the past,
but your sister
has the original manuscript.

Sisters share their memories
of childhood – days on the beach
and visits to the zoo.
Loved books and playthings,
pets they knew and loved.
Disasters, excitements, victories.
The smell of home.

A sister can calm your fears
– because she knows where they began.

You commandeered my computer
and at times my text books.
My pens and protractor
were at your disposal.
You hogged the land-line.
But then I would never
have got through Physics
if it hadn't been for you.

Or History.
And you introduced me to Mozart
And lent me your Chanel.
So I can't grumble.
And if I didn't thank you then,
I thank you now.
You are my sister and you
changed my life.

We drift with time,
until one day
we find ourselves strangers in a world
we barely recognize,
a world of new technologies and customs,
fashions, speech.
And feel our own world
lost and forgotten.

Until we turn and see our sister
and our brothers disguised
like us in saggy, baggy skins,
and see they are the same
as when we were all very small.
That we carry all the selves
we've ever been within us
and cannot be touched by Time.

Whatever the differences
sisters help each other out.

In hard times
I would have
toppled over
– if you hadn't
held me up.

I've a few skills –
some rather odd
– and they are all at your disposal.
Any time.

Acts
of
Kindness

SISTERS GROW MORE DEAR
WITH TIME
— THE YEARS ARE LIT BY ACTS
OF KINDNESS
AND BY REMINISCENCE.

One learns the art
of sharing and kindness
with a sister.

She'll not waste time with words
– but get down to the practicalities.
Which may entail
a bed for the night,
a loan, a doctor, a lawyer.
Or simply some shrewd
and uncomfortable advice.

Far away...

Who do I phone when something
wonderful happens? You, of course.
It's not one half so wonderful
if you do not share it.

Time and distance
have no effect on sisters
who love each other.

I often feel she is there with me
when I have an exciting or new experience.
I'll think, "Oh she would love this."

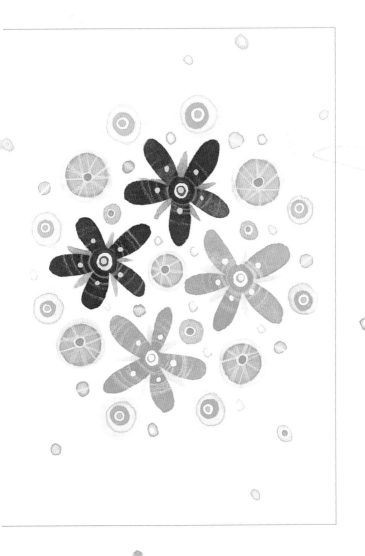

LOVE
BOND

There will be greater loves
– but none so deeply rooted
as that between siblings.

She's part of me
and I am part of her.
Until the ending of our days,
we will be part of one another's lives.
However far apart, however
different, we are essential
to each other.

So close.
So dear.
My sister.

To have a sister
is to have an extra pair of eyes,
an extra pair of ears
and an extra pair of hands.

In a perfect world everyone
would be issued with a sister.
To share delights and sorrows.
To always be there.
To be with you forever.

You live in my life.
I live in yours.

You have been my companion,
my best friend, all my life.
I need you.
I hope you need me too.
Together we can deal with
anything that comes!

What is a
Helen Exley® Gift Book?

Helen Exley has been creating gift books
for more than twenty-seven years, and her
readers have bought more than 108 million
copies of her work in thirty-seven languages.
Because her books are bought as gifts,
she spares no expense in making sure that
each book is as thoughtful and meaningful
a gift as it is possible to create:
good to give, good to receive.
Team members help to find thoughtful
quotations from literally hundreds of sources, and
then the books are personally created.
With infinite care, Helen ensures that each spread
is individually designed to enhance
the feeling of the words and that the
whole book has real depth and meaning.

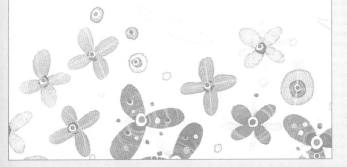